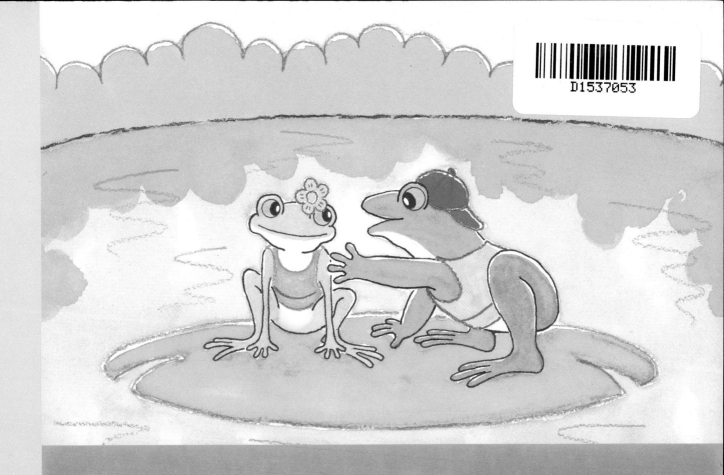

"Tag, you're it!" says Bob.

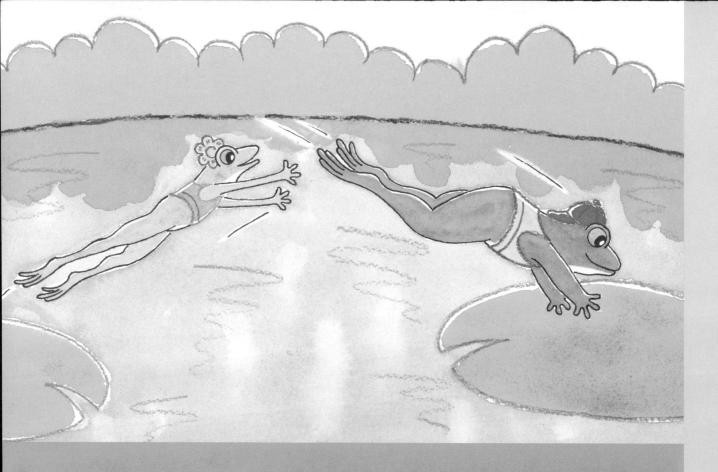

Lucy chases Bob.

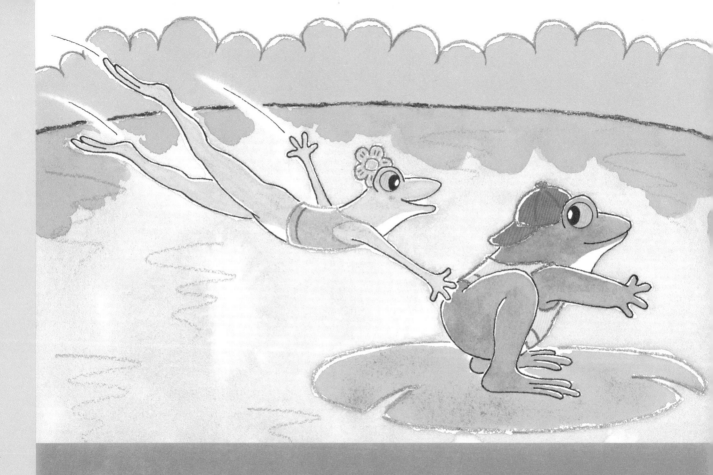

"Tag, you're it!" says Lucy.

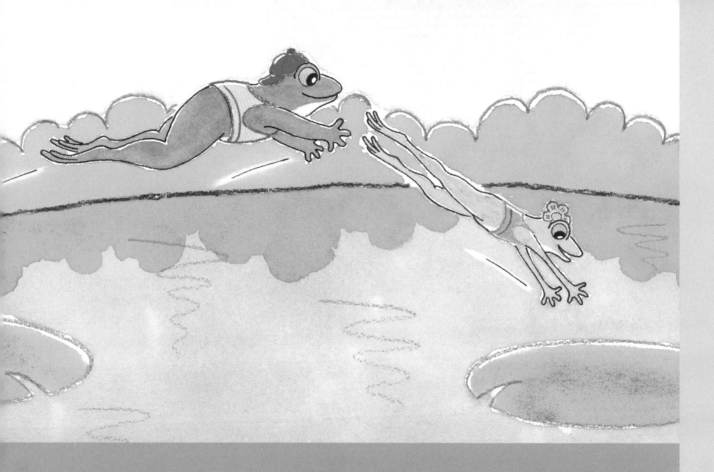

Bob chases Lucy.

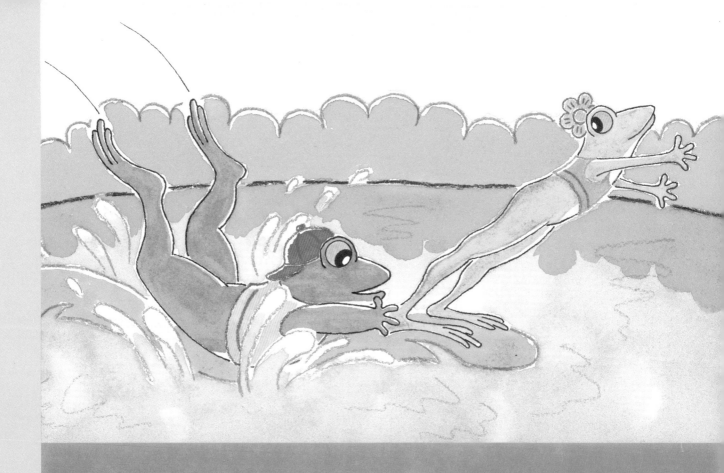

"Tag, you're it!" says Bob.

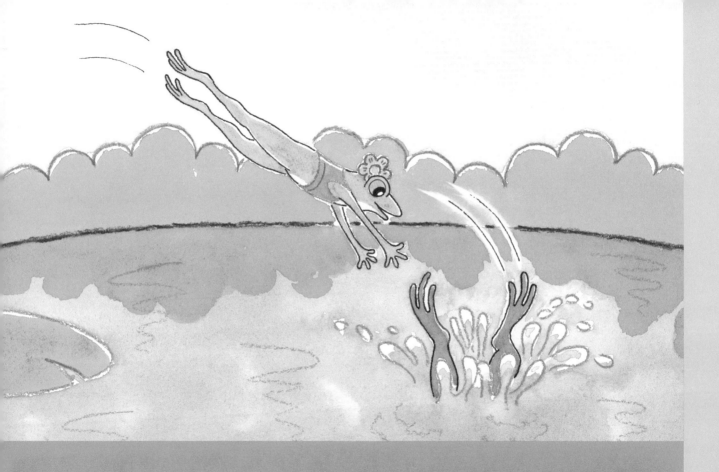

Lucy chases Bob.

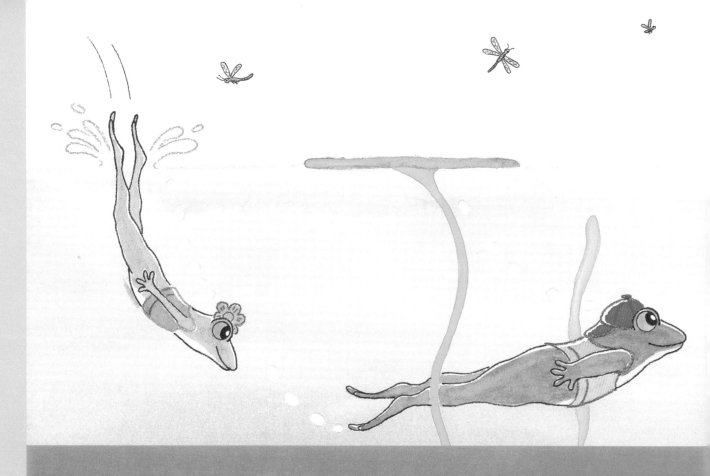

Lucy chases Bob underwater.

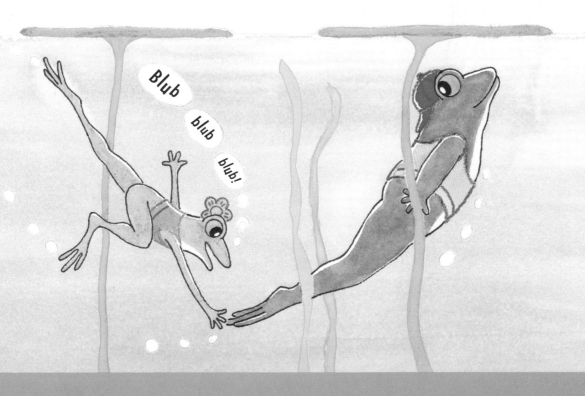

"Blub, blub blub!" says Lucy.